HEINEMANN MATHEMATICS 1

Name

WORKBOOK 6

Subtraction to 6

Revised

1

Cars

**Put on 4 cars.
Take away 1.**

**How many
are left?**

**Put on 5 cars.
Take away 3.**

**How many
are left?**

Buttons

Put on 5 .
Take away 4.

How many are left? ☐

Put on 6 .
Take away 1.

How many are left? ☐

4 take away 3 = ☐

5 take away 2 = ☐

8 take away 4 = ☐

6 take away 4 = ☐

7 take away 3 = ☐

9 take away 5 = ☐

Blast off!

Put 5  in the rocket.

Take away 5.

5 take away 5 = ☐

3 take away 3 = ☐

6 take away 6 = ☐

4 take away 3 = ☐

1 take away 1 = ☐

4 take away 4 = ☐

6 take away 5 = ☐

2 take away 2 = ☐

Spots

Put on 6 spots. Take away 3.

$$6 - 3 = \boxed{}$$

6 take away 5.

$$6 - 5 = \boxed{}$$

5 take away 1.

$$5 - 1 = \boxed{}$$

7 take away 4.

$$7 - 4 = \boxed{}$$

8 take away 3.

$$8 - 3 = \boxed{}$$

$$3 - 2 = \boxed{}$$

$$6 - 3 = \boxed{}$$

5

10 Plates

$$10 - 1 = \boxed{9}$$

$$9 - 1 = \square$$

$$8 - 1 = \square$$

$$7 - 1 = \square$$

$$6 - 1 = \square$$

$$5 - 1 = \square$$

$$4 - 1 = \square$$

$$3 - 1 = \square$$

$$2 - 1 = \square$$

$$1 - 1 = \square$$

Fried eggs

10 eggs.

Eat 2 eggs.

$10 - 2 = \boxed{}$

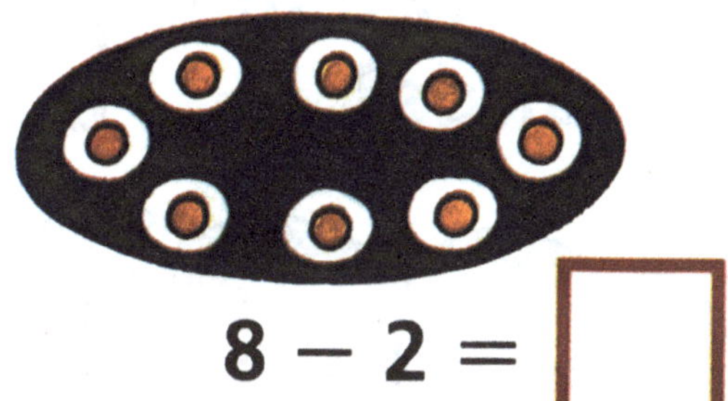

$8 - 2 = \boxed{}$

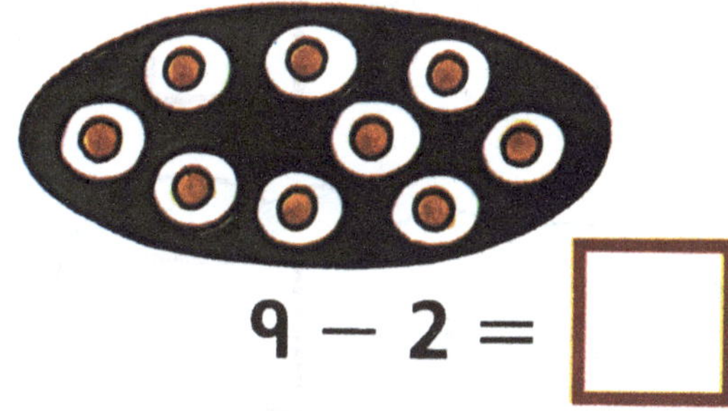

$9 - 2 = \boxed{}$

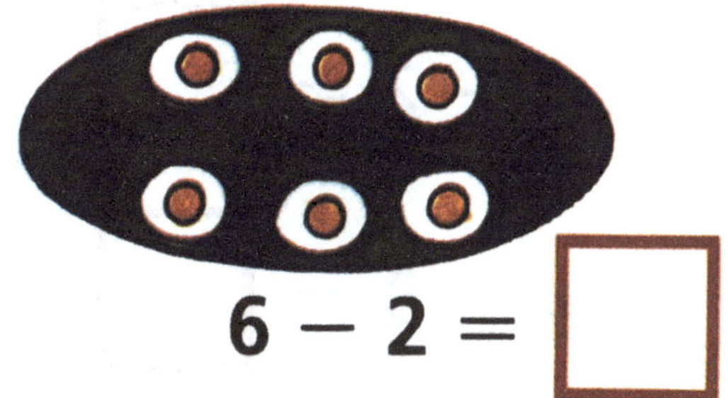

$6 - 2 = \boxed{}$

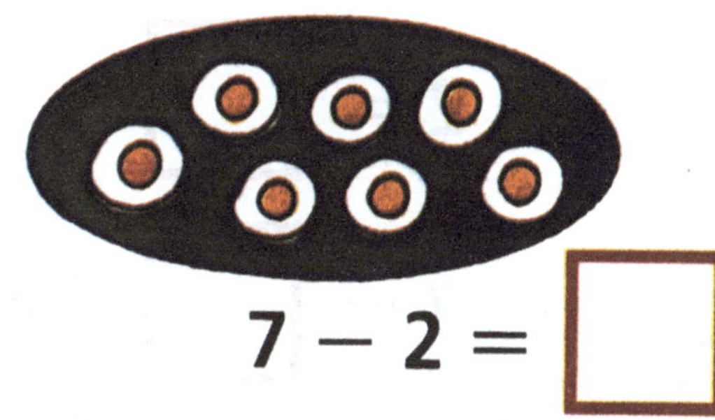

$7 - 2 = \boxed{}$

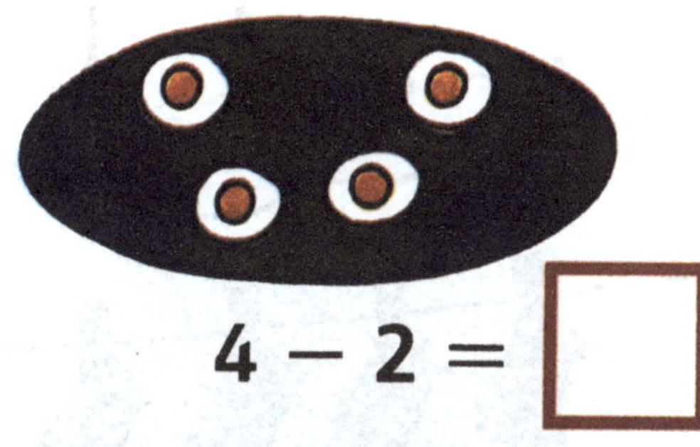

$4 - 2 = \boxed{}$

$5 - 2 = \boxed{}$

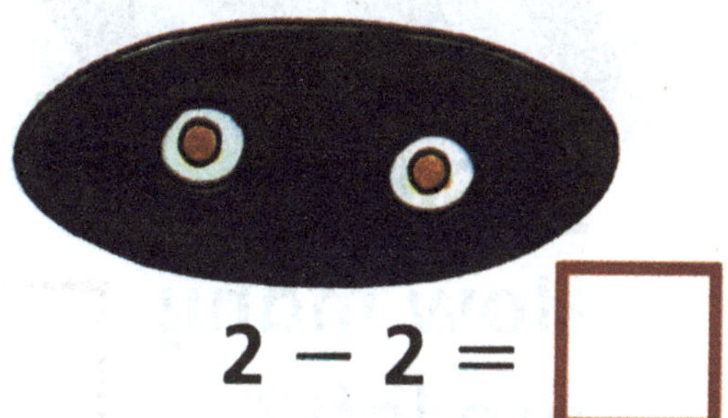

$2 - 2 = \boxed{}$

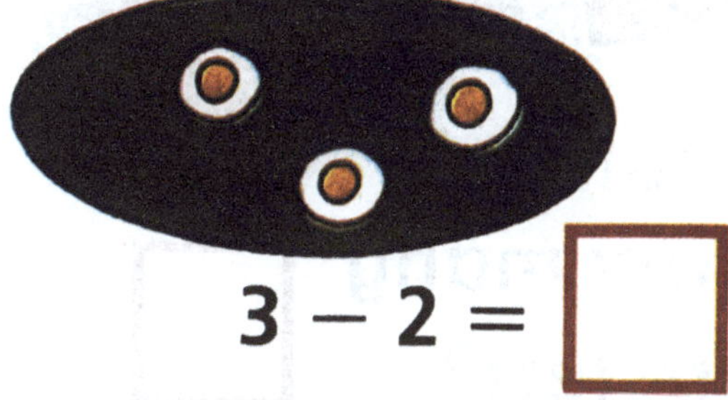

$3 - 2 = \boxed{}$

Flying

How many planes? ☐

How many birds? ☐

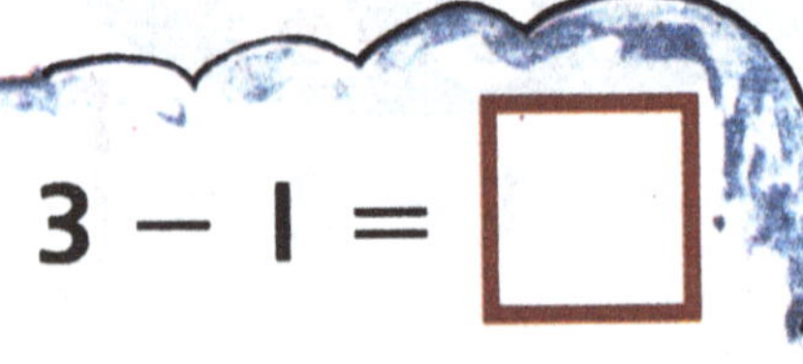

$3 - 1 =$ ☐

$3 - 2 =$ ☐

$3 - 3 =$ ☐

$4 - 1 =$ ☐

$4 - 2 =$ ☐

$4 - 3 =$ ☐

$4 - 4 =$ ☐

1 falls off. How many are left? ☐

2 fall off. How many are left? ☐

The pond

How many ducks in the pond?

Hide 1 duck.   5 − 1 =

5 − 2 =

5 − 3 =

5 − 4 =

5 − 5 =

5 − 4 =

5 − 5 =

4 − 3 =

5 − 3 =

2 swans fly away.

How many
are left?

Bubbles

$6 - 1 = \boxed{}$

$6 - 2 = \boxed{}$

$6 - 3 = \boxed{}$

$6 - 4 = \boxed{}$

$6 - 5 = \boxed{}$

$6 - 6 = \boxed{}$

$6 - 4 = \boxed{}$

$6 - 1 = \boxed{}$

$6 - 2 = \boxed{}$

$6 - 5 = \boxed{}$

Dog show
5 − 4
6 − 1
5 − 5
6 − 6
5 − 3
5 − 2
6 − 4
6 − 2

II

Pet shop

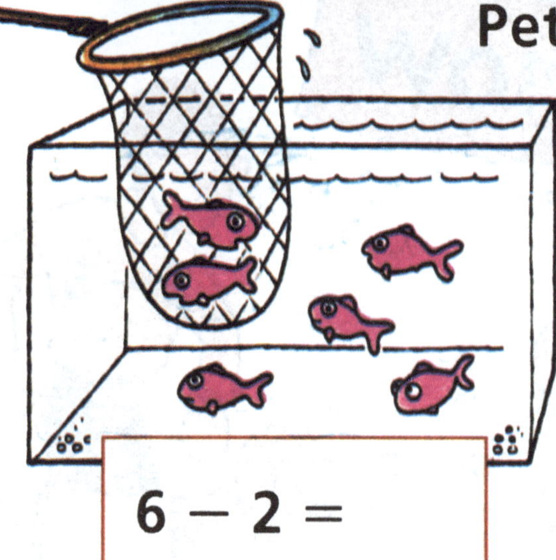

6 − 2 =

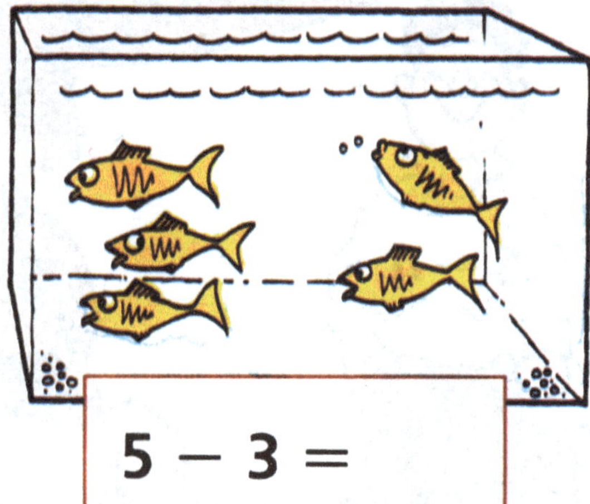

5 − 3 =

3 − 1 =

4 − 3 =

6 − 3 =

2 − 2 =

4 − 1 =

R8

Pet shop

How many are left? 

How many are left? 

How many are left? 

3 get out.

How many are left? 

R 9

Jumble sale

Each has **6p** to spend.

How much is left? ☐ p

How much is left? ☐ p

How much is left? ☐ p

How much is left? ☐ p

How much is left? ☐ p

How much is left? ☐ p

R 10, 11

Jane's Jumble

Take off 2p

Take off 3p

Match

1	2	3	4	5	6	7	8	9	10	11	12	13	14	15

Heinemann is an imprint of Pearson Education Limited, a company incorporated in England and Wales, having its registered office at Edinburgh Gate, Harlow, Essex, CM20 2JE.
Registered company number: 872828
ISBN 978 0 435 03087 2 © Scottish Primary Mathematics Group 1991.
First published 1991. Revised edition 1995.   25   28
Typeset and illustrated by Oxprint Design. Printed and bound in Great Britain by Bell & Bain Ltd, Glasgow

ISBN 978-0-435030-87-2